If You Like Hazel

If You Like Hazel

by Ted Key

NEW YORK · E. P. DUTTON & CO., INC. · 1952

The cartoons in this book have appeared in The Saturday Evening
Post and copyright by The Curtis Publishing Company as follows:

1949: pages 7, 12, 25, 26, 27, 28, 30, 31, 32, 60, 71, 72,
73, 75, 76, 77, 78, 79, 81, 82, 83, 92, 93, 94,
96, 97, 98, 103, 104, 109, 111, 116, 118, 119,
122, 127.

1950: pages 18, 24, 33, 34, 37, 42, 43, 50, 51, 52, 53, 54,
55, 56, 57, 58, 59, 61, 62, 64, 65, 66, 67, 68,
69, 70, 74, 80, 88, 89, 90, 91, 95, 99, 100, 105,
107, 125, 128.

1951: pages 3, 6, 8, 9, 10, 11, 13, 14, 15, 16, 17, 19,
20, 21, 22, 23, 29, 35, 36, 38, 39, 40, 41, 44,
45, 46, 47, 48, 49, 63, 84, 85, 86, 87, 101, 102,
108, 113, 114, 117, 123, 124.

1952: pages 106, 110, 112, 115, 120, 121, 126.

The Artist gratefully acknowledges permission granted by
The Curtis Publishing Company to reprint them.

Library of Congress Catalog Card Number: 52-10427

FOR
GERT, HANK AND LEN

"Hi"

"Dead bird."

"Detective did it."

"THAT BUM A HOLDOUT?"

"Deduct one and one half per cent from *WHOSE* wages?"

"One at a time. Where's this gang?"

". . . called courtship. Then they get married, 'Do you,' 'I do,' and so forth. Then they take a honeymoon, like a vacation, only better. Then they drive home. And *THEN*, brother . . ."

"Oh-oh . . ."

"That's rumba?"

"SHE'S HAD KITTENS!"

"Ever hear of a sinker ball?"

"Look pal . . ."

"Who's the dame?"

"Fair and warmer with variable northeasterly . . ."

". . . and on my mother's side, the de
Laceys, there were a general, two senators,
a justice of the Supreme Court, a . . ."

"Results of the fifth race at Jamaica . . ."

"I'll count to ten. ONE."

"TWO."

"THREE."

"FOUR."

"FIVE."

"SIX."

"SEVEN."

"EIGHT."

"N-I-I-I-NE!"

"TEN."

Ted Key

27

"Who does the **arithmetic** at your joint?"

".... cook the meals, do the dishes, wash the clothes, scrub the ..."

"YES?"

"Why do we like Hash-o? Twenty-four words or less?"

"It's been so long,
dear. Better ask
your father."

"Little weak on
fractions. Ask
your mother."

". . . which leaves
four and a half; you
watching this? . . ."

"What'd he get in television?"

"Coming through."

"I'm glad you asked me that question, senator.
World conditions aren' good because . . ."

"Dinner is served."

"Gave 'em homework the first day!"

"Eight in the side pocket, ten in the corner, twelve in the . . ."

"Using the fan?"

1

2

3

4

Ted Key

"Forgot our keys."

"Grand Central Station."

"An end-around towards home."

"You're out of gas."

"YIPE! !"

"... bringing the right shoulder in contact with ..."

"There go the chrysanthemums."

"May I comment?"

"Just waxed."

"And nothing in this hand . . ."

"Change?"

"HE'S ON THE ROPES!"

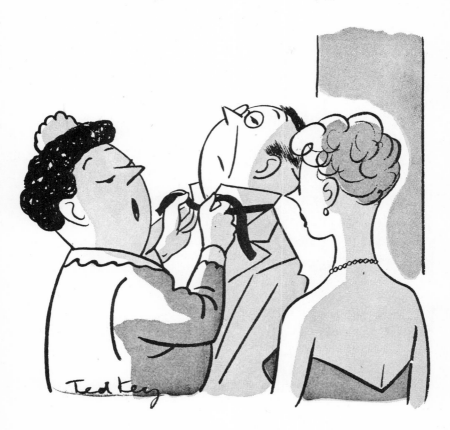

"Then take this end . . ."

"Who scored?"

". . . sort of what you call a tomboy. So when this smart
aleck picked on my brother, I got my slingshot . . ."

"Great!"

"That noise you thought was a firecracker . . ."

"Wrench"

"Imagine! Ten years in the house
and didn't know he had termites!"

"I have news for you."

"Shall we try that again?"

"Man's best friend over here loused up the flower bed."

"Big deal."

"YEOW!"

". . . where they plan to honeymoon at the bride's es-
tate in the Bahamas. Upon their return to this coun-
try—OH, DEAH ME—they will reside at the groom's
summer home in Newport, while their winter . . ."

"Cut the meat balls in half?"

"Neck too."

"Gesundheit."

"Second half. Cotton Bowl."

"Gonna save a lot of marriages."

"Well—I'm off!"

"Washable?"

"No seconds."

1.

"Smile when y' say that,
pardner." "I'm a smilin' . . ."

2.

". . . a round of the news. We now take
you to London, England, where . . ."

3.

". . . conducted by Arturo Toscanini.
And now, from Tschaikovsky's . . ."

4.

". . . man on second, two away, last
of the seventh. Musial at bat . . ."

"Boy, are we on a sucker list!"

"COMPANY!!"

"It's not that I don't appreciate your desire to help."

"How long will you be? Wanna put the steak on."

"Thousands of people batting their
brains out to bring us electricity."

"SEVEN-THIRTY-EIGHT! !"

"Be back for dinner, I presume."

"Are *YOU* kidding?"

"Ready?"

"Can't read it on the roof, y' know; better
get down here with another newspaper."

"Stepping out?"

"... keeping the left arm straight ..."

"But here's the difference. Where the book says butter, I use . . ."

"Sounds important."

". . . to properly assemble this train . . ."

"We'll make it an old-fashioned Thanksgiving. All the children, of course, and bring Aunty and Uncle and Cousin Jane and . . ."

"Three kids and a dog."

"Defrosting the refrigerator?"

"No sooner sit down . . ."

"Some enchanted evening . . ."

"OKAY, OKAY, COMING! Rings that bell as if . . ."

"Once you get the knack of it . . ."

"Don't touch anything."

". . . miss your voice all through the day,
my buddy, MY BUD-DY . . ."

"Sharpening the scissors?"

"Stay within yelling distance."

"JUST ONE!"

"How big was this frog?"

"Little Bear follow Strong Heart. Thunder Cloud angry."

"How about . . . ?"

"Dying"

"KICK! !"

". . . with this difference—in *canasta* . . ."

"Brace yourself."

"Won't go the full seven games, and I'll tell you why . . ."

"Tell them the one about the Englishman,
the Irishman and the . . ."

". . . However, if hair does *not* appear within thirty days, return the bottle and we will gladly . . ."

"Now then, the pitcher throws to
the catcher—still with me?—who . . ."

"I've had a LONG, HARD busy day."

"Smoke upstairs, smoke downstairs, smoke . . ."

"When *I* say bedtime . . ."